SASHA visits SINGAPORE

Illustrated by Alpana Ahuja
Written by Shamini Flint

Book Five: Sasha in Asia

Sasha is in Singapore with her Mamma.

They decide to go for a bumboat ride down the Singapore River.

Sasha and Mamma catch a boat on Boat Quay.

They drift past old shophouses and busy restaurants.

Sasha waves to the people on the banks of the river!

Sasha and Mamma have a wonderful view of the city from the river mouth.

"Can you see that beautiful old building in front of the skyscrapers, Sasha?"

Sasha is more interested in the water-spouting statue.

"What's that, Mamma?"

"It is the Merlion, Sasha. It has the head of a lion and the body of a fish!"

That afternoon, Sasha and Mamma visit the Singapore Zoo.

Many creatures roam freely around the zoo.

Other animals are separated from visitors by wet or dry moats.

Sasha spots two very unusual tigers.

"Mamma, those tigers are not black and orange - they are black and white!"

The next morning, Sasha and Mamma visit the Jurong Bird Park.

There are hundreds of different species of birds at the park.

"Which bird do you like best, Sasha?"

"I love the colourful macaws, Mamma. Especially that big blue one!"

"That is a Hyacinth Macaw, Sasha."

Can you see it?

"What are we going to do next, Mamma?"

"We are going to visit an old friend who lives in Singapore, Sasha."

"She has a daughter who is your age!"

Sasha and Mamma take a taxi to a lovely old colonial house.

It has large windows and wooden shutters.

There is a frangipani tree with fragrant pink flowers growing in the garden.

Mamma takes Sasha and her new friend to the Night Safari.

They hop on a train that is painted in zebra stripes!

Sasha sees the yellow eyes of many animals shining in the dark.

Can you spot them?

"Mamma, what are those large, long-nosed animals?"

"They are tapirs, Sasha. Tapirs are nocturnal creatures."

The next morning, Sasha and Mamma visit the Singapore Botanic Gardens.

Sasha is enchanted by the lush greenery and exquisite tropical flowers.

"Sasha, look over there. It is a statue of a girl on a swing."

She looks like she is having fun!

Sasha and Mamma spend the afternoon on Sentosa Island.

They ride the walkway through Underwater World.

"Mamma, it is like being under the sea!"

Sasha spots a curious dugong, sleek sharks and a stingray gliding quietly through the water.

Can you see them?

The next morning, Sasha and Mamma go shopping on Orchard Road.

"Look, Sasha. It's a lion dance."

Sasha is amazed to see the lions leaping about acrobatically.

They are dancing in time to the crashing of cymbals and the beating of gongs.

"Mamma, I can see the dancers' legs!"

Later that day, Sasha and Mamma set off for Changi Airport.

It is crowded on the train. There are people reading, listening to music and snoozing.

Sasha is sad to be leaving Singapore but she is looking forward to her next trip!

Where do you think Sasha will go next?

Sasha visits
the Botanic Gardens

Sasha visits the Zoo

Sasha goes Shopping

Sasha visits Sentosa Isl

Sasha visits the Bird Park

Sasha visits the Museu

Also available online at www.sunbearpublishing.com

Sasha visits Bali

Sasha visits
Kuala Lumpur

Sasha visits Hong Kong

Sasha visits Bangkok

Sasha visits Singapore

Sasha visits Beijing